THE BIG ACHOO!

A guide for training children in sensory modulation

BY DAFNA WARM (SANDLER)

Illustrator: Mirel Goldenberg

Translator: Mark Elliott Shapiro, Byron Seminars

ISBN: 9798733918860

This book is dedicated to

My father Samuel (Monty) Sandler of blessed memory,
who taught me how to laugh

My mother Shoshana, who taught me how to read

My son Ori, who taught me how to write

My daughter Noa, who taught me how to stick with the task

My daughter Adi, who taught me how to accept

My husband Ron for inspiring me

And my dear sisters Orit, Tami and Efrat

Publish and printed in USA, 2021

Ori's father had a very strange Achoo, oh my,
And no one really knew why.
When he sneezed, everyone seemed to hear him:
The whole apartment building, the whole street,
the whole neighborhood, the whole city,
Even Grandma Rose from Jerusalem,
which was very far away, Because Ori lived in Tel Aviv.

His Achoo would happen without any warning.
For example, when everyone was seated
At the dining table for the family supper,
Suddenly, we heard his Achoo
Without any early alert, without any "Head's Up"-er

His Achoo was a roll of thunder
And the whole building seemed to shudder.

A-a-a-a-a- ACHOO
O - o - o - o - o - o -!!!

The Achoo would echo through the building for about five minutes,
And all the neighbors from the first floor to the top floor would answer
in unison:
"Bless you! Bless you!"
And he would reply, "Thank YOU! Thank YOU!
I hope you weren't disturbed by my Achoo!"

Bless you

His Achoo was deafening, like the boom from a thundercloud,
And for Ori, who always sat beside him,
his dad's Achoos sounded really loud.
In order to protect his eardrums
 (not a musical instrument but a sensory organ)
He would stop his ears and would prevent them from ringing.
That's what you have to do when you hear sounds that are deafening.

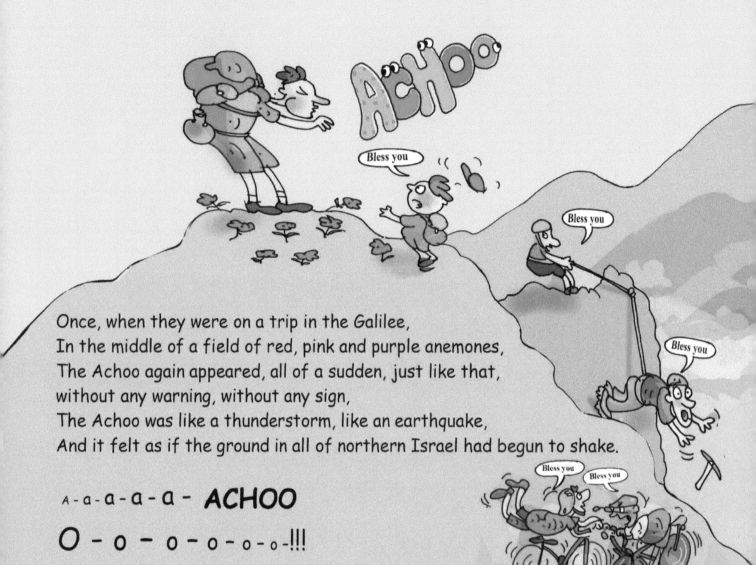

Once, when they were on a trip in the Galilee,
In the middle of a field of red, pink and purple anemones,
The Achoo again appeared, all of a sudden, just like that,
without any warning, without any sign,
The Achoo was like a thunderstorm, like an earthquake,
And it felt as if the ground in all of northern Israel had begun to shake.

A - a - a - a - a - **ACHOO**

O – o – o – o – o – o -!!!

The echo of that Achoo was heard for at least five minutes,
And all the vacationers from the Galilee in the north to Eilat in the south answered in unison:
"Bless you! Bless you!" And he replied,
"Thank YOU! Thank YOU!
I hope you weren't disturbed by my Achoo!"

This time his Achoo was really loud,
Ori, who stood close to his father, had to distance himself,
because to be too close would have been outrageous
He was afraid that his dad's Achoos were contagious.
In order to protect his eardrums
(which are thin membranes that allow us to hear)
And to prevent his ears from ringing,
he would plug his ears.
That's what you have to do when you hear sounds that are deafening, remember?

This time Ori noticed something really strange:
In the middle of his dad's

A-a-a-a-a- ACHOO
O - o - o - o - o - o -!!!

The earth started to tremble – what a sight!!!
The anemones closed their petals out of sheer fright,
And the birds froze in mid-flight.
After the storm had passed, you could again look up at the sky
And Ori felt a single teardrop fall from his eye.

"Daddy," Ori pleaded, "your **Achoos** boom like a thundercloud,
And the echo, my dear Dad, is twice as loud.
Please put a stop to these **Achoos**, I beg you,
How can I invite any of my friends to our house?!
I feel so embarrassed, Daddy, I really do!
I ask you, wouldn't it be preferable,
But only if you are able, to lower your sneezes a decibel,
Or two? Then your Achoos won't be heard in the whole neighborhood.
Only the neighbors in this building will hear you. Wouldn't that be good?"

His father answered: "I'm sorry to cause such a problem.
But my sneezes just happen all of a sudden – I can't stop them.
I agree, I do have a strange Achoo,
But frankly I don't know what to do!

"Grandpa Mike, you know, sneezes loudly, too:

A-a-a-a-a – **ACHOO**

O – o – o – o – o-o-!!!

"Okay, maybe his **Achoos** are lower by a decibel or two,
And maybe they're a little easier on the ears, too.
But this Achoo has for generations been in our family,
And I must admit, my son, it's really a part of me.
There's nothing I can do about it.
This Achoo is me, this is who I am, I'm telling you."

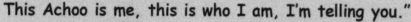

Despite Ori's pleas, his dad continued to loudly sneeze.

Unfortunately for Ori, the **Achoos** became **louder** -

the same old story – **But much stronger!**

Like the trumpets' blaring sound,
Like the drums of war beginning to pound.

Ori was really frustrated.
He didn't know what to do,
but he decided that he would have to try something,
So he whispered to his dad:
"Daddy, if you want to talk to me, and I know that you do,
Then please speak English and stop speaking Achooish."

"Listen, Daddy, I have an idea. Let's play 'Small Achoo and **Big Achoo**'!
Let's start with a tiny, really quiet A-a-Achoo-oo-oo."

His father tried, tried with all his might,
But his Achoo still sounded fright- full:

A - a - a - a - a - ACHOO
O – o – o – o – o – o – o !!!

"Okay, could you try a **Medium-Sized Achoo?**
Not too loud and not too quiet?"

His father tried, tried with all his might,
But his Achoo was still loud and fright- ful:

"Okay," Ori continued, "let's try something else:
Now give me **huge, mighty sneeze**.
I'm sure you can do it. So please sneeze, please!"

A - a - a - a - a - **ACHOO**

O - o - o - o - o - o - o -!!!

Of course, his dad's sneeze Sounded loud and clear.

"Daddy, could you again please try a tiny, really quiet A-a-Achoo-oo?"
His father closed his eyes and concentrated really hard:

A - a - a - a - a – **ACHOO**

"Daddy, at last you did it – a medium-sized Achoo!" Ori was delighted.
"A medium-sized Achoo!!!"

But, after a while, despite all Ori's efforts, it could be seen
That his father had forgotten what he'd learned and had returned to his old routine.
Ori was disappointed. He was angry with his dad and was again frustrated.
"I see you're sad," his mother said,
But, frankly, your father's Achoos just make me laugh!"

Let's try to laugh when we hear your dad's **Big Achoos**.
Let's speak Achooish:

A - a - a - a - a - **ACHOO**

O – o – o – o – o – o - o -!!!

Now let's do it together one more time:

A - a - a - a - a - **ACHOO**

And then Ori and his mom laughed and kept on laughing.

Ori's Dad was lying on the sofa in the next room.
He heard them talking.
Their words made him freeze.
My Achoos," he said to himself, "really bother them, I can see.
The next time I feel an Achoo, I'll grab that naughty sneeze
Before it manages to run away from me!"
Maybe I'll put my hand on my nose, maybe two hands, or more.
Or maybe I'll put it in my pocket so it won't get away
And then I'll make sure that this is where it'll stay!"

The next morning Ori woke up bright and early.
His father was hugging his mother
and they were whispering to each other.
Ori tiptoed toward them and then he heard his father sneeze:
"A-Achoo!" That sneeze was small and weak.
It wasn't loud like thunder. It created no echoes.
His dad's sneeze was quiet, perhaps even too quiet. It was weird.

"Something's missing," Ori said to himself.
"There's no echo, it lacks rhythm, it lacks melody!

"That is definitely not my father's **Achoo!**"

My dad is such a happy guy and his smile is so sunny.
My dad's sneezes were always so merry, so musical, so funny!

This is my dad's sneeze

That's my daddy, my daddy, my daddy!

Ori jumped up and down; he was so full of joy.
"Bless you-ou—ou"
He said out loud.
And Daddy replied, **"Thank YOU! Thank YOU!"**
"I hope you weren't disturbed by my Achoo"

"Daddy," Ori added, "without your **Big Achoo**,
You will be an ordinary dad, like everyone else's dad,
and you won't be a special, unique dad.
And now Ori no longer felt sad!
His father was overjoyed: "Come here, Ori,
I want to give you a **Big Hug**! A hug from a daddy who really loves you."

Ever since that day, his dad's **Achoo** never changed!
Usually, it wasn't too quiet but it also wasn't too **loud**.
It was just a **medium-sized sneeze**.
When Ori is worried about something or just tired,
then his dad's **Achoo** sounds **loud as thunder**,

Even though the sneeze is really not so loud.
And when Ori is relaxed and feeling just fine,
he can't even hear his father's sneezes.
when his father's Achoo is really tiny and barely heard,
Ori just smiles and sometimes he laughs.
Just to be sure, Ori continues to give to his dad
A **big hug** and **a** kiss – to show him he is so glad!

And one more thing: When Ori's father meets with his friends,
they know they should cry out "Bless you!" when he sneezes,
Because now his Achoo is neither big nor small,
only medium-sized, only medium-sized.

A guide
for parents, nursery school/ kindergarten, teachers and therapists

**A few words on sensory modulation
and on how to get the most from this book**

Professional consultants: Dr. Miri Tal Saban, Ph.D., and Tomer Aharoni, M.Sc.

Table of contents

Introduction

This guide touches on a variety of subjects, such as meeting the Other, the difficulty involved in sensory modulation and in modulating activities, our ability to change the behavior of the Other, and accepting the Other. The guide, which deals with each subject separately, should however be considered as a single unit and the different chapters should thus be seen as complementing one another.

Prologue
The story of two mothers[1] and two infants with sensory modulation difficulties

Dalia's infant

Dalia: "I so much looked forward to giving birth to my first child. Every mother is familiar with this feeling of anticipation. For months, I experienced excessive joy mixed with trepidation: What sort of infant will I give birth to? Will that infant be "normal"? What kind of mother will I be?

Her first child was not at all a disappointment. When he was born, he seemed to be well acquainted with his new world. He was a beautiful baby with a real "presence." She hugged him when he cried; however, he did not stop crying. Only after a few days she understood what was going on: She was unable to calm him down! Whenever she tried to pick him up, he began to cry. Although she knew that every baby cries, she had to confront a difficult experience: "I am unable to do anything that can stop my baby from crying! I feel very frustrated!"

And how did her newborn infant feel about this state of affairs? If he could already speak at such a tender age, we would probably have heard him say: "Nobody understands me. Where am I? What is this place that I have arrived at? What are these people doing to me? What is going on? Instead of calming down, they are only making me feel miserable!"

The growing frustration on both sides could give rise to painful thoughts in the minds of any parents, especially new ones. Thoughts, such as "I have failed as a parent! Or "I cannot calm down my own infant child! What does that say about me?" This kind of frustration can cause new parents to lose all confidence in their parenting abilities.

---

[1] All the names appearing here are not the true names of the individuals referred to.

Fortunately, Dalia had a strong intuition about her situation: "Perhaps my child is sensitive to being touched. In that case, what should I do? Should I avoid physical contact, should I stop touching him, or, on the contrary, should I hug him and keep on hugging him? I'll have to experiment." And that is what she did. After a few days, he stopped screaming when she picked him up and hugged him. She felt relieved because she could now hug her child. Although he did not smile when she touched him, at least he did not begin to cry. And that was indeed progress. After two weeks, her hugs managed to calm him down. She now said to herself: "My hugs do calm him down. It might take a while but my hugs are having a calming effect." In the meantime, she began to see a professional who led her to understand: "Congratulations! My child was born with a sensory modulation problem!"

Micky, Esther's son

Esther related that her son Mickey displayed severe behavioral problems. From the moment he was born, he cried when he was hugged and he bawled when he was even touched. Why was he reacting like this? Esther did not know the answer. When she touched him to calm him down, her touch only made him feel frustrated. Her infant boy's sensitivity to being touched was so extreme that she found it impossible to feed him straight from the bottle and she was forced to do so in an unnatural manner by having him lie on her while feeding. She then tried something else: She laid him down on several pillows that propped up the bottle so that he drank from the bottle without her directly touching him.

**

How similar Esther's and Dalia's infant sons are, and yet how different. If Esther had known that her son had a sensory modulation problem, she could have managed to feed him directly from the bottle. Perhaps he could have received the hugs that every infant needs, even if, from the moment he was born, he showed signs of being repelled by hugs.

If you are familiar with such stories, this book is for you. Its aim is to give you the professional background to this problem but it is first and foremost a therapeutic tool in the form of a story that your children will love and will, at the same time, help them cope on a daily basis with their thoughts, insights and reactions.

This book is intended to provide you with the professional background to this sort of problem, and to offer you advice, exercises, suggestions and explanations. At the end of this guide, you will find tips on how to get the most from this book.

I hope that you will enjoy reading the guide and that you will find it helpful.

Chapter 1 – Sensory modulation : Profile

Modulation is the ability to graduate or adjust your response in accordance with the information you are receiving from your surroundings.

What is sensory modulation?

Sensory modulation is a central process of information processing that includes all our sensory systems; it enables children to moderate and adjust their response to sensory stimulation and to avoid extreme patterns of behavior.[2] Normal sensory modulation influences the quality of life for children and adults in various fields of functioning. In order to properly grasp the significance of sensory modulation, imagine a dam on a river whose function is to regulate the quantity and direction of the river's flow. As long as the dam functions properly, it effectively adjusts the quantity and direction of the river's flow. But what will happen if the dam stops functioning properly? What will the effect be on the quantity and direction of the river's flow?

What is sensory modulation disorder (SMD)?

An impairment of our sensory modulation means an impairment of our ability to adjust the intensity and character of our behavioral responses to sensory stimuli in accordance with the demands of the particular activity in which we are engaged and in accordance with the demands of our particular surroundings. Such an impairment means that we respond with a level of intensity that is not commensurate with the level of intensity of the particular sensory stimulus: for example, an infant crying when embraced by his/her mother.

Sensory modulation disorder (SMD) is indicated by the presence of symptoms that are so severe that they disrupt the routine of our lives and the activities of children or adults.

Among children, (SMD) can impact their emotional, social, perceptual and sensorimotor development[3] can seriously affect their ability to function in general and can even sometimes make it difficult for them to become socially acceptable.

----
2 Miller, 2004, Bundy and Murray, 2002
3 Dunn, 1977b.

The three main types of sensory modulation difficulties [4]

Sensory Over-Responsivity

Children with sensory over-responsivity react in a disproportional manner to sensory stimuli, and their response to such stimuli is more intense than is the case with children who do not have this problem. Children with sensory over-responsivity find sensory stimuli unpleasant, frightening and sometime even painful. Sensory over-responsivity is sometimes also referred to as sensory defensiveness.

Over-responsivity can be confined to only one of our senses or it can include a number of them. Children with this problem at times express discomfort when wearing certain clothes or refuse to wear certain types of fabric. They are fussy eaters, do not like to be in playgrounds and are afraid of auditory stimuli, even moderate auditory stimuli.

The neurological picture of children with sensory over-responsivity is that their level of arousal to sensory stimuli is higher than it is among "normative" children. The sensory stimuli around them are "registered" by their nervous system in a more intense manner than the normative level. Since their responses are particularly acute when confronted by unexpected stimuli, their reactions might at times be quite extreme: They might find themselves repelled by the stimuli, might have angry outbursts, might start to cry and might find it difficult to adjust to transitions and to sudden changes.

Sensory Under-Responsivity

children with sensory under-responsivity are often unusually quiet and passive. They either ignore sensory stimuli in their surroundings or do not react to them at all. Sometimes they appear highly introverted and communication with them is difficult. At times they will give the impression of being apathetic, drowsy or indifferent and may appear to lack the inner drive most children have toward socialization and motoric inquiry. Frequently, children with sensory under-responsivity require a particularly intensive stimulus in order to become actively involved in their surroundings, in the task they are performing or in their interaction with others.

Sometimes these children will not react when they are hit by something, when they fall or when they suffer cuts or bruises; this lack of response could be dangerous because they might not be able to feel pain, such as when they suffer skin injuries through contact with very cold or very hot objects.

----

4 Miller, Anzalon, Lane, Cermak and Osten, 2007.

The neurological impression is that sensory stimuli are "registered" in the nervous system of children with sensory under-responsivity in a less intense manner than among other children; thus, we say that children with sensory under - responsivity have a lower level of arousal as opposed to other children. We can use the term "impaired register" in order to describe children with this problem. In extreme cases, they do not seem to be capable of discerning the sensory data around them or of even "registering" it.

In the case of children with sensory under-responsivity, their parents' awareness of this problem is of critical importance. Frequently we tend to ignore children with this sensory pattern, thinking that they are "good babies" or "easy-to-manage children" because they make no demands, when, in point of fact, they need more supervision than other children.

Sensory Seeking

Children with such a sensory pattern are constantly in search of sensory stimuli. They long for such stimuli with what borders on obsessiveness, and they seem to have an irrepressible impulse for sensory input. They engage in activities or do things that are meant to give them additional sensory stimulation in a continual attempt to satisfy their drive or impulse for sensory stimulus.

They tend to be in constant motion, they bump into others or into objects or into walls, and they always seem to be jumping up and down. They might perhaps need to hear loud music or to watch television with the volume turned up and they may tend to focus on stimuli or people who offer them visual stimulation. They will constantly want to try out new flavors or aromas, to engage in tactile experimentation, to hear sounds that are louder and of longer duration than what children with normal sensory responsiveness would find acceptable.

In surroundings where children are expected to sit quietly, such as in a classroom, a movie theater or a library, children who are "sensory seekers" will find it difficult to satisfy their need for constant stimuli. They might be impulsive, almost on the point of "exploding" emotionally, as they attempt to meet the quota of sensory stimulation they require.

Awareness of a sensory modulation problem

It is important to be aware of difficulties that children might have in sensory modulation. If there is the suspicion that your child might have a sensory modulation problem, you should arrange for an early diagnostic test with an occupational therapist or an occupational therapy clinic. If your child is diagnosed as having a sensory modulation problem, therapeutic intervention and the adjustment of the home and school settings will have a significant impact on his/her development.

Therapeutic intervention and the adjustment of a child's home and school settings will reduce his/her frustration and the feeling of "a lack of success" that the child and his/her parents may be experiencing. In this way, both parents and children can stop spending time and energy on dealing with the problem and can move forward in order to ensure the children's normal development, growth and scholastic progress.

The aim of this kind of approach is to provide the child with a program of meaningful activities and a controlled level of stimuli that are suited to his/her level of development and targeted at his/her needs.

The child can thereby be taught how to express an "adjusted reaction"; as a result, there will be a marked improvement in the capacity of his/her nervous system to process sensory data in a modulated manner that has been adjusted to the child's particular surroundings. It should be noted that surroundings that encourage the provision of opportunities for sensory stimulation are of vital importance for children with impaired sensory modulation.

In many cases, the child might have more than one characteristic of impaired sensory modulation. Thus, the child's behavioral picture might include several such characteristics: sensory over-responsiveness combined with sensory under-responsiveness, or, alternatively, sensory seeking in one sensory system or in a number of sensory systems simultaneously.

The connection between a sensory modulation problem and emotional modulation difficulties

Children with a sensory modulation problem sometimes find it difficult to modulate their emotions. Their responses are not modulated and at times these children appear to be displaying an excessive or an inadequate emotional response. In some cases, they also develop a behavioral modulation problem.

Emotional modulation difficulties

Children with an emotional modulation problem are characterized by a difficulty in expressing their feelings and in effectively managing them. At times they express their emotions more intensely and more frequently - and at times less intensely and less frequently – than what is normally acceptable. Sometimes it is hard to understand the connection between the circumstances and the intensity of the emotion these children express.

Behavioral modulation difficulties

Children that have problems modulating themselves feel that the world is not a pleasant place in which to live, that it is unpredictable and that it is even hostile toward them. They might display behavior patterns characterized by a lack of mental flexibility, by an unwillingness to cooperate with others, by attempts to exert control in certain social situations or by extreme oppositional patterns. Their difficulties in modulating themselves, in tuning their behavior and in adjusting to different situations at times are expressed in behavioral problems. One of the commonest behavioral problems is a difficulty in making transitions and in moving from one activity to another, that is, a difficulty in ending an activity that the child particularly enjoys (such as watching television or playing video games) in order to engage in another kind of activity that he/she enjoys less.

To better understand this kind of behavior pattern, try to imagine that you are a driver competing in a racing car competition and that, at the very moment your car goes into high gear, you have to stop in the middle of the racing course and set off to study for an exam.

Turning a problem into an advantage

In today's modern world, the characteristics of non-modulated children (impulsiveness, a tendency to cry a lot, etc.) are considered problematic. Initially, we might think that we do not need such traits. Nonetheless, it is possible to reinforce, teach and encourage children with a sensory modulation difficulty because these are actually positive characteristics that one must know how to use and because it is possible to channel such characteristics into skills that can ensure success in a modern setting. For example, highly sharpened senses can be converted and developed into characteristics of leadership and creativity.

Chapter 2 – Principles and tools: Modulating activities

Some children need to be calmed down while others need to be pushed to arousal. Children require stimuli that are suited to their particular needs in order to help them to modulate the sensory system in their body.

All these activities must be performed under the constant supervision of an adult who is in eye contact with the children and they must be carried out gradually and moderately. It is highly recommended that **an occupational therapist or an occupational therapy clinic** be consulted before the initiation of these activities.

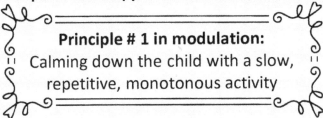

Principle # 1 in modulation:
Calming down the child with a slow, repetitive, monotonous activity

When we want to focus on calming down children with sensory modulation problems, we should lead them in an exercise involving both the controlled use of resistance power and a repetitive, slow, monotonous activity. We can incorporate in that exercise a soothing song that has a slow rhythm and which is played at a low volume. For example, we can improvise on a well-known children's song, for example, "Danny is relaxing in the hammock" or "Dana is lying on her bed."

Relaxing activity achieved by means of a deep stimulus

In order to attain a deep stimulus, heavy motor work should be performed.
Heavy motor work, which provides deep input to the body (proprioception), including the joints, by means of deep pressure. Receptors in the joints help promote sensory modulation.

Examples of relaxing activities:

Wheelbarrow walking – The children support themselves with their hands while an adult holds on to their legs.

Dragging and loading – Of shopping bags from the supermarket and schoolbags to the car (in a moderate manner).

Martial arts – Karate, judo and capoeira classes that work on deep stimulus and which develop children's ability to control their body and their emotions

Caterpillar, cocoon, butterfly – Let's crawl like a caterpillar, then turn ourselves into a cocoon and stand where we are. Now, let's fly like a butterfly.

Playground – We will rock ourselves in a hammock, we will go up ladders, we will climb up the slide (and thus we will utilize the resistance of the force of gravity).

A relaxing activity that relies on touch: The magic massage

Relaxing activities relying on touch are very important for children with a sensory modulation difficulty. In addition to the relaxing effect itself, a massage develops for these children a sensory "picture" of their own body. Your body absorbs data from its sensory systems and constructs for itself a sense of its internal body scheme. Initially, the parents of the children will help them to relax and, at a later stage, the children will learn how to relax on their own.

Additional advantages to relaxing activities that rely on touch
- Reinforcement of the bond between parent and child
- Reinforcement of eye contact (when the children are lying on their back)
- Reinforcement of the children's body self-image
- Recognition of one's body borders and body scheme. The recognition of his/her body's borders reinforces the development of the child's ego, perception of identity, and self-esteem (just as a country defines itself through its borders). In addition, the child learns where his/her body begins and where it ends. One can utilize this window of opportunity to speak about personal space, privacy and the body's borders: Where one can touch and where one must never touch.
- Relaxation and calming-down
- Release of endorphins (which serve as a natural tranquilizer) in the brain
- Reinforcement of the child's self-image and self-confidence
- Sensory modulation – deep proprioceptive pressure (gradually applied touch)
- Improvement of the child's ability to concentrate
- Improvement of the child's sleep quality (in the case of children who do not get a good night's sleep)

In what part of the body can one provide a relaxing activity relying on touch?

In every one's body (one must avoid touching the child's private parts, of course) it is important **to focus on the joints** (wrist joints, the joints connecting our arms to our shoulders, etc.). Our joints have many neurons (nerve cells), where data is received in the brain and where the nerve processing occurs. **You must avoid touching the spinal column**. The child's face and head should be touched gently.

When is it suitable to perform a relaxing activity that relies on touch?

It is recommended that there should be a set ritual when the child goes to bed. In addition, if children are restless during the day, instead of being angry with them, you can suggest a relaxing activity that relies on touch: "I see that you are restless. You need to do some squeezing and pressing activities. What should we prepare together? How about a pizza? That sounds like a delicious idea, right?"

The goal is to enable the children ultimately to learn how to recognize on their own when they are restless, moody or fidgety and to know how they can calm themselves. For example, they will know that pressing on their joints can have a relaxing effect.

Ideally, how much time should be spent on relaxing activities that rely on touch?
It is sufficient to perform such activities only for a number of minutes, although, of course, activities that are performed over a considerable period of time are preferable.

Examples of relaxing activities:

Magic massage – This activity is suitable as a ritual when the child goes to bed or in the middle of the day as a means of helping him/her to relax. The child can lie on his/her stomach on a bed, a mattress or a puff pillow. The parent or the responsible adult places the palms of his/her hands on the child's shoulders and slowly moves the palms along the length of the child's body: from the shoulders and the back (one must avoid contact with the child's spinal column) to the thighs, the legs and the palms of his/her feet. One can then move on to the child's face and head, both of which should be touched gently). The massage should take the form of slow, long, deep and gradual movements of pressure. (One can accustom a sensitive child to such massages in a gradual manner.)

It is recommended that a soothing song should accompany the massage. One can invent words and apply them to a well-known melody): "Danny, my sweet Danny, Danny, you can now relax after a week of activity" or "Dana, my sweet Dana, you are closing your eyes, you can rest now." Or you can play some pleasant, relaxing background music.

"Ironing" – The parent slides his/her hands along the sides of the child's body slowly, maintaining a deep touch in all his/her movements.

Gradual touching – The child can be covered with a sheet or a light/thick blanket; the fabric should be pleasant. The pressure can be applied either through the blanket or directly to the child's body in accordance with the latter's wishes. If the child finds it difficult to accept the direct contact of the parent's hands, the touching should be performed gradually: Initially, the child's body should be covered with a pillow or a blanket while the parent applies gentle pressure, and then the pillow or blanket should be replaced by a lighter blanket or a sheet until the child becomes accustomed to direct contact with the palms of his/her parent's hands.

The imaginary "pancake" game – The child lies down on a mattress that has been placed on the floor (or on a blanket). The mattress or blanket should be placed at right angles to the child's body (to create the form of a cross). While the child's torso will lie on the mattress, his/her head and legs will not be on the mattress and will not be covered.

The child should be asked, "What do you want us to prepare? Pizza? Pancakes? Ice cream?" The parent or responsible adult begins to roll the child's body and to wrap the blanket around the child's body. The child's body should be rolled carefully and afterwards the pressure movements should be deep (again the touch should be deep) or the parent can slowly drum his/her fingers on the child's body.

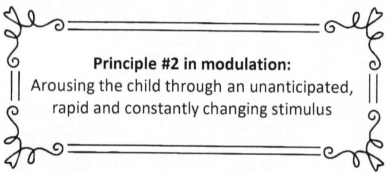

Principle #2 in modulation:
Arousing the child through an unanticipated, rapid and constantly changing stimulus

When we want to work on **arousal**, it is recommended that we apply an unanticipated, rapid and constantly changing stimulus. An appropriate song for arousing the child can be incorporated in this exercise; the song should have a fast beat and should be sung or played at high volume. For example, the parent can sing, "Danny is swinging on the swing," or "Dana is jumping up and down in the circle."

Examples of arousal activities:

Various sports activities – Basketball, soccer, football, ball games

Imaginary paths – Jumping like a kangaroo, hopping like a frog, leaping like a tiger

Playground – Slide, swing, merry-go-round, trampoline

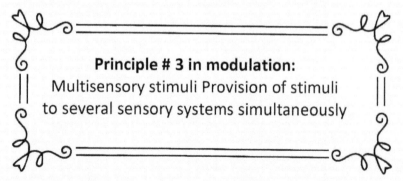

Principle # 3 in modulation:
Multisensory stimuli Provision of stimuli to several sensory systems simultaneously

Multisensory activities that involve more than one of our senses work on the body's kinetic system and sensory system (vision, hearing, taste, smell, touch) and their goal is to achieve an equilibrium between arousal and calm.

Examples of multisensory activities:

Exposure to sensory musical instruments – that generate multi-sensory stimulation: For example, wind chimes, gong, ocean drum, cabasa, piano, rainstick, darabouka, drum, cymbals.

Cooking (under an adult's supervision) – A multisensory activity that involves all senses: vision, taste, smell, hearing (the sound of a knife slicing a vegetable, the sound of bubbling liquids, etc.) and taste. Cooking and baking are very enjoyable activities that give children a sense of control as well as teaching responsibility and improving their ability to organize themselves and their time and resources and to follow instructions. Children who are not overwhelmed by stimuli should be given a gradual introduction to the art of cooking. Actions such as slicing vegetables or fruit help train the child in the skills of initiating and stopping action.

Vegetable garden - Let your children irrigate, hoe, dig and plant vegetables and trees. Let them get wet, let them touch the earth and get dirty, let them feel and 'knead' the soil. The vegetable garden is a golden opportunity for turning on all our senses. The "fruits" and vegetables that you and your children will cultivate in your garden will soon appear.

Performing various tasks in the playground – Go with your child to the swings. Your child should try to alternately swing hard and fast then slow and gentle, while improvising on a well-known children's song , "Swinging, swinging. Up and down. Down and up." The singing should be done in accordance with the intensity and speed of the swinging: hard and fast, or slow and gentle. Afterwards you and your child should go to the merry-go-round and try to alternate between spinning around quickly and spinning around slowly. You can both sing a Hebrew song associated with the Jewish festival of Hanukkah, "Dreidel [Hanukkah spinning top], dreidel, spin round and round" or "The merry-go-round spins around wherever it can." The singing should be done in accordance with the intensity and speed of the spins on the merry-go-round: Hard and fast, or slow and gentle.

Paths at home – Spread pillows on the floor. Then ask your child to hum on a kazoo a tune that he/she particularly likes as he/she walks among the pillows (children who find it difficult to hum on a kazoo can instead sing a song and then hum it). The intensity of the humming on the kazoo and the rhythm of the tune should match the pace of the activity and its nature. If the activity is energetic and fast-paced, the humming on the kazoo should be loud and with a quick rhythm. You and your child should hop over the pillows barefoot and then jump over them. During the jumping and the hopping, the humming of the kazoo should be fast-paced and strong. Now, put the kazoo aside and hum or sing a melody. Lie down both of you on the floor with your hands at your side and slowly roll over again and again. Finally, you and your child should crawl on the floor between the pillows. During the rolling over and the crawling. you should both hum in gentle. slow tones.

Taking a break beside the children's desks – Ask the children to sit on a chair. You can place a wobble cushion (either one with a prickly fiber or one with a rough surface, depending on what you prefer) and have the children sit on it. Incorporate music for listening that is partly fast-paced with a strong beat and partly slow and sedate. During the musical segments that are fast-paced with a strong beat, ask the children to drum the floor with their feet at a hopping or galloping pace (while remaining seated). During the musical segments that are slow and sedate, ask the children to place their feet on the floor and to raise their bodies from the chair using their hands. Examples of suitable music: Hungarian Waltz no. 2 by Brahms, or Csardas by Monti.

Invent your own exercises – Create your own exercises involving multisensory stimuli.

Mapping of sensory modulation difficulties in accordance with zones in the human body and the adjustment of sensory modulating activities:

Every child with a sensory modulation difficulty has certain zones in his/her body that are characterized by more sensory modulation difficulties than in other zones.

Stage 1: Map out the sensory modulation difficulties and locate the zone in the body that requires stimulus.

Stage 2: Prepare together with your child a unique toys-and-games box for the particular zone in the body that has a sensory modulation difficulty. For example, if your children experience a sensory modulation difficulty related to their mouth, a box with toys and games related to the mouth can be prepared together with them.

Let's take any box of suitable size, such as a shoe box. We will decorate it together with the children and make sure that the decorations attest to its contents: For example, for children who have a sensory modulation difficulty related to their hands, we can paint handprints on the box with gouache and then write the children's names in big letters on the box. For children with a sensory modulation difficulty related to their mouth, we can decorate the box with kisses or candies.

Stage 3: Your children will need mediation in their selection of a toy/game or a stimulation tool from the box when it is required. For example, instead of saying to your child, "Please don't chew your sleeve," you can suggest a toy/game from the box of mouth-oriented toys/games that you have already prepared.

Stage 4: Your children will soon learn what toy/game they should choose from the box in order to calm down before they turn to their previous default, such as chewing their sleeve.

Stage 5: The use of the box will gradually diminish.

The activities should be suited to the children's age and to the extent of their ability to use stimulation tools/methods. It is always recommended that an occupational therapist or occupational therapy clinic should be consulted if a child's sensory modulation difficulty is impairing his/her level of overall functioning.

It is also recommended that the box should be used and the activities carried out in accordance with your family's particular schedule or the schedule of your child's educational setting. For example, there should a unique toy/game for morning hours, afternoon hours and evening hours.

Characteristics of children with a mouth-related sensory modulation difficulty

Children with a mouth-related sensory modulation difficulty like to put things in their mouth and they like to talk a lot. They do not like to brush their teeth, love/hate certain fabrics and flavors, are fussy eaters, often raise their voice when they are talking, find it difficult to stop using a pacifier, sometimes drool, and sometimes, they bite or spit.

The sensory modulation of the child's mouth will influence the modulation of the child's entire body at the physical and emotional levels.

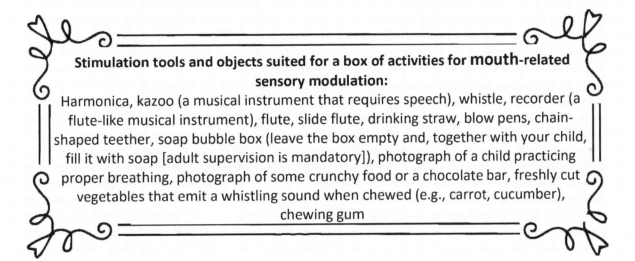

Stimulation tools and objects suited for a box of activities for mouth-related sensory modulation:
Harmonica, kazoo (a musical instrument that requires speech), whistle, recorder (a flute-like musical instrument), flute, slide flute, drinking straw, blow pens, chain-shaped teether, soap bubble box (leave the box empty and, together with your child, fill it with soap [adult supervision is mandatory]), photograph of a child practicing proper breathing, photograph of some crunchy food or a chocolate bar, freshly cut vegetables that emit a whistling sound when chewed (e.g., carrot, cucumber), chewing gum

Characteristics of children with a hand-related sensory modulation difficulty

Children with a hand-related sensory modulation difficulty like to touch things; touching things calms them down. They are relaxed when they are climbing, they avoid being touched, they love/hate strong hugs, they tend to shove other children, they love/hate to feel certain fabrics and textures.

The hands of children with this difficulty are the most active organs in their body during the day and thus their hands often reflect the degree to which these children are restless/calm. The sensory modulation of the child's hands will mean that the child will generally be calmer.

Stimulation tools and objects suited for a box of activities for hand-related sensory modulation:
Small spiky ball; stress ball for squeezing; objects with different fabrics for sensory modulation and for touching: feather, pieces of cloth, modeling clay, dough, pipe cleaners, cotton wool, sponges of various textures for kitchen cleaning chores, pompoms, playdough (for creative activity); paper shapes punches, gloves, xylophone and other percussion musical instruments that require manual dexterity, dominoes, rainstick, Chinese percussion box, etc.

Other ideas for working with children who have a hand-related sensory modulation difficulty:

Book of "finger songs" for young children: Hebrew songs such as "I have ten fingers," "Raise your hands above your heads," or English songs like "Head, shoulder, knees and toes" or "The itsy-bitsy spider climbed up the water spout."

Multisensory artistic activities that involve several of our five senses: playing an instrument; singing; dancing; painting/drawing with various materials: pastels, watercolors, gouache, finger painting (in the bathtub)

Homemade sandbox for use inside the home: Preparation of a sandbox from a shoe box or from a plastic container and the insertion of wet sand (only when the sandbox is made from a plastic container), dolls or plastic soldiers for hand stimulation and for activation of the child's imagination.

Playing melodies on wind chimes: The child plays a melody and then suddenly stops. What happens when the chimes keep ringing? In order to stop the chimes completely, the child will have to "hug" the chimes and to hold on to them.

Characteristics of children with a leg-related sensory modulation difficulty

Children with a leg-related sensory modulation difficulty continually and restlessly move their feet whether they are sitting or standing. They constantly get up from their chair, jump up and down in a manner that displays a lack of adjustment to their setting and kick their feet a lot, or, alternately, they are passive, do not like to move around very much and do not explore their setting with the same intensity that their friends display.

   Children with this difficulty might develop psychomotor problems, be continually restless and might find it hard to complete tasks and to meet the demands of their surroundings.

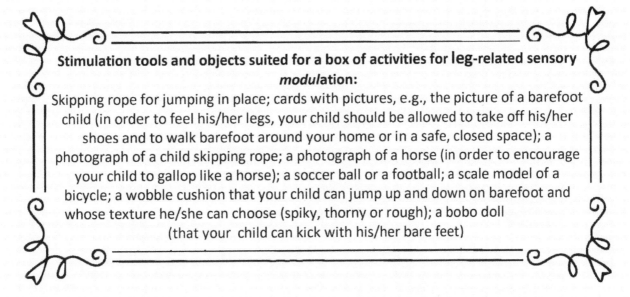

Stimulation tools and objects suited for a box of activities for leg-related sensory modulation:

Skipping rope for jumping in place; cards with pictures, e.g., the picture of a barefoot child (in order to feel his/her legs, your child should be allowed to take off his/her shoes and to walk barefoot around your home or in a safe, closed space); a photograph of a child skipping rope; a photograph of a horse (in order to encourage your child to gallop like a horse); a soccer ball or a football; a scale model of a bicycle; a wobble cushion that your child can jump up and down on barefoot and whose texture he/she can choose (spiky, thorny or rough); a bobo doll (that your child can kick with his/her bare feet)

Characteristics of children with an ear-related sensory modulation difficulty

Children with an ear-related sensory modulation difficulty are very sensitive to loud noises or are attracted to loud voices, yell when they talk, frequently plug their ears and avoid noisy places. They might develop emotional, social, behavioral and cognitive problems. One can accustom these children to loud noises by gradually exposing them to loud noises.

Characteristics of children with an eye-related sensory modulation difficulty

Children with an eye-related sensory modulation difficulty avoid eye contact, are sensitive to certain colors or look for them, are attracted to strong colors or to certain shapes, are activated by visual stimuli. They see the world through unmodulated glasses and it is therefore important to expose them to suitable stimuli.

Characteristics of children with a head- or hair-related sensory modulation difficulty

Children with a head- or hair-related sensory modulation difficulty bang their heads against the railings of their playpen; throw their heads on the adult who lifts them up; press their heads against the wall; stand on their head; suspend themselves upside down from chairs, sofas and railings; pull their hair out. They find it difficult to function in general.

Stimulation tools and objects suited for a box of activities for head- or hair-related sensory modulation:

Combs; hairbrushes; "Magic Hair Brush" (to free knots in your child's hair – you should brush your child's hair gently so that the action of combing or brushing will be a kind of massage for his/her head); bandanas; hats with different textures (some children like to wear wool hats because then they feel that their head "is held more securely"); photograph of a gentle head massage

Characteristics of children with a nose-related sensory modulation difficulty

Children with a nose-related sensory modulation difficulty are very sensitive to strong smells or seek them out. Their sense of smell must be modulated in order to enable them to function during the day.

Stimulation tools and objects suited for a box of activities for nose-related sensory modulation:

Small cloth bags in which dry leaves of spice and aromatic plants such as rosemary, mint, parsley, cloves, have been placed. A soap bar can be peeled with a vegetable peeler to create aromatic soap flakes to be placed in the cloth bags; another soap bar can also be placed in one of the bags. On the subject of breathing- yoga cards with instructions for breathing exercises, and the alternate closing of each of your child's nostrils (for older children and under an adult's supervision). Your child can gradually be exposed to aromas and can play the game "Guess what aroma this is?"

Principle # 4 in modulation:
Teaching your child how to "play and stop"

This principle relates to the ability to suddenly and unexpectedly stop doing something.

Sensory modulation games: These games work on the principle of sensory modulation – which is intended to teach your child how to suddenly stop doing something, without any advance preparations – and create a humorous effect. The goal of the games: To teach your child how to stop doing a wanted activity in order to engage in an unwanted activity and to also teach him/her how to modulate him/herself.

The "achoo" games

- Let's do a big achoo, let's do a small achoo, let's do a medium-sized achoo. This is a game on a graduated continuum – weak-medium-strong – and is based on the difference between very weak and very strong. It helps the child to modulate him/herself.

- Let's do a strong achoo and then we will suddenly stop sneezing when the signal (which has been agreed upon in advance) is given. Let's do a gradual achoo: From a small achoo to a big one, from a weak achoo to a strong one (crescendo), and then the reverse: from a big achoo to a small one, from a strong achoo to a weak one (diminuendo).

- We can encourage our child to participate in artistic activities and to suddenly stop performing them: for example, to play music or beat a tune, with a maracas, or a xylophone, and then to suddenly stop playing or beating the tune; or to sing and then to suddenly stop singing. Such games offer an excellent opportunity for enriching your child's vocabulary with new terms and their significance: strong-weak, fast-slow, rough-smooth, etc.

- **"Imitation of a rhythmic pattern" game** – Your child will repeat a certain rhythmic pattern. This kind of activity requires the child to learn how to listen and pay attention in order to exactly reproduce a rhythm and in order to know when to stop singing or playing a tune.

- **"Artistic imitation" games** – Your child will be asked to repeat certain coloring patterns, using a marker pen or crayons. He/she will then use gouache tubes to copy horizontal and vertical lines, diagonal lines, dots, circles, spirals, etc.

- **"The conductor of the orchestra" game** – One of the children is chosen to be the conductor of an imaginary orchestra and he/she will signal to the other children, the "members of the orchestra," how to play or sing: weak/strong/fast/slow. The children learn how to modulate themselves. The child playing the role of conductor is given the opportunity to exercise control and to suddenly perform a certain action; these are skills that children with a sensory modulation difficulty require.

- **"Find the missing beat"** or the **"Music minus 1" exercise** – The children have to continue singing a song that has been suddenly stopped. This kind of game creates tension. For example, the Hebrew song, "The little rabbit forgot to close the door, /The poor thing caught a cold and his nose started running. La-la-la." The adult abruptly stops singing and the children continue the song with "Achoo!" They can also sing English songs such as "Old MacDonald had a farm" (you suddenly stop singing and the children must answer "Ee ay ee ay oh") or "If you're happy and you know it, clap your hands" (you suddenly stop singing and the children must clap their hands).

  The game demands that the children pay close attention, be precise and adjust to a new situation. In addition, it enables a broad use of humor that every one- – children and adults alike – will enjoy. This activity requires a certain level of sensory modulation from both the "adult who is asking the question" and the "child who is answering the question." Both the adult and the child must take turns singing, stopping to sing and waiting for an answer.

- **The traffic light game** – Cards in three different colors: red, yellow and green. The children engage in an activity: running, dancing, jumping up and down, etc. When the adult shows them the red card, the children must stop what they are doing; when they see the yellow card, they get ready for the next stage in the game; and, when they see the green card, they continue the previous activity.

- **Learning "to release" instead of "stopping"** – This game involves looking at things closely (internal contemplation). After we have tried other "stop and go" games, let us try something else: Instead of stopping, we will release something. For example, we will try to release an idea that we very much want: We will breathe deeply and slowly. The breathing exercise will "release" the thoughts that had been stuck and which focused on the stimulus that we very much wanted.

Many children's games are based on sensory modulation

The statues game – The children move through the room to the tunes of a recorded melody, to the beat of a drum or to the sound of a metronome. When the melody, beat or sound stops, the children stop moving and "freeze," becoming statues. Games like ocean-mainland, musical chairs, "Simon says" ("Herzl said" in the Israeli version) and others are based on sensory modulation.

What is the difference between acting impulsively and acting quickly? You should try to act quickly but you should avoid acting impulsively. The difference between acting impulsively and acting quickly is the ability to modulate impulsiveness and to plan in advance.

What is the difference between patience ("orech ruach" in Hebrew: literally, a "length of breath") and impatience ("kotzer ruach" in Hebrew: literally, "shortness of breath")? The Hebrew language helps us in our attempt to modulate our children and offers the following suitable expressions:

Patience is "orech ruach" (literally, a "length of breath") – We certainly need "ruach aruka" (literally, a "long breath") if we want to be considered patient. In other words, we have to learn how to breathe slowly and deeply in order to develop modulation. Proper breathing helps promote modulation. We can use the meaning of these two expressions in order to explain to the children the idea of patience: Patience or "orech ruach" ("length of breath") is expressed by deep breathing, while impatience or "kotzer ruach" ("shortness of breath") is expressed by quick, short breaths.

What is the difference between talking loudly and yelling when you talk? Children who always yell when they talk find it difficult to modulate the power of their voice and speed of their speech. We can teach them how to speak slowly and thus to speak more quietly. We can help them learn that skill with the help of a metronome. We can read a story slowly, moderately or quickly, according to the beat of the metronome, and we can thereby teach them to be aware of the speed of their speech, to the vital need to take a breath every few seconds when speaking ,thus they can then learn how to speak more quietly. We can ask them: "At what speed do you usually speak? What speed do you like? What speed is nicer to hear?" In this way, we can help them to develop an awareness of the speed of their speech and to take a breath every few seconds when speaking, and we can also remind them to speak more slowly (without making any reference to the volume of their voice).

Chapter 3 – The worldview behind the story "The Big Achoo"

Contemplation – "All in the ear of the listener": What the listener hears

The story raises a number of questions: What is the difference in the extent of movement between planned, controlled behavior and unplanned, uncontrolled behavior? To what extent can we control our behavior? Can behavior be altered? Is there a need for change? Who should make the change? With regard to the story, we can also ask: Who should make the change? Ori's father? Ori? Both of them? How will they make the change?

The narrative "behind the scenes" of the story "The Big Achoo" deals with the question: **What is the best way to deal with the behavior of the Other if that behavior bothers us?** For example: How does Ori deal with his father's thundering sneezes? When we take a close look at this element in the story, we can help children to think about the dilemma from another vantage point. They can use the knowledge that they have internalized from the story in order to solve conflicts in their surroundings within their family setting and their educational setting.

The story presents a certain human phenomenon:

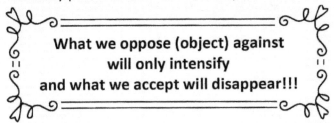

**What we oppose (object) against
will only intensify
and what we accept will disappear!!!**

The "achoo" in the story is a metaphor representing an impulsive physical reaction, that is, an involuntary physical reaction, an automatic action or a pattern of human behavior that we display without thinking about it. We do not need to invest any thought or to engage in any deep discussion in order to get rid of a bit of dust from our nostrils. This position helps us to learn how to accept the fact that there are some things we cannot control! The story emphasizes the point that the solution to a problem sometimes depends on **our acceptance** of that problem.

When we are in a family setting, we often find ourselves in a situation where we must accept something different, something that is connected to the Other, even when that something really irritates us. For example, the disturbing behavior of one of the members of our family, such as the Other's irritating voice, loud sneezes, restlessness or impulsiveness. According to the approach that is illustrated in this story, we may discover that, if we accept a disturbing pattern of behavior, we can achieve what we want regarding that pattern: its disappearance.

How can we accept the unpleasant behavior of someone else?

How do we arrive at a situation where we can actually accept the loud achoo?
If we take a close look at the achoo in the story from a different perspective, we may discover that the achoo is a natural healing mechanism that is intended to quickly release a foreign element (such as dirt or dust) that could obstruct our respiratory system.

You should make the children realize that, in certain instances, we can change our approach.

The story illustrates an important lesson: We cannot control every situation. We must change our approach, forget about trying to control a situation and stop criticizing it. Instead of adopting a judgmental position toward the Other, we should examine our criticism, remind ourselves that it attests to something inside us that is bothering us and then ask ourselves what that something is.

In the Babylonian Talmud, Tractate Kidushin, p. 70b, we read **"When we criticize a flaw in someone, we are actually criticizing a flaw in ourselves."** When children read the story, we must try to find out what factor in the behavior of the Other bothers them. For example, do they like or hate their own achoo? Are they afraid that their own achoo bursts out without their being able to control it? Is there any other element in their own behavior that they themselves do not like? Not every conflict between ourselves and someone else is necessarily what it seems. Sometimes it is a conflict that exists within us and which affects the way we feel about other people in our lives.

Strategies for dealing with the conflict that is illustrated in the story

We should explain to the children that in every situation they always have several options. Thus, in every situation, they must weigh their various options and decide what the most suitable one for them is.

Avoidance (the proactive strategy)

Avoidance encourages a pattern of distancing oneself from a particular stimulus and prevents one from actually coping with a situation. The purpose of the strategy of avoidance is to distance ourselves from a confrontation that will lead us to feel pressure. For example, you avoid visiting a field of flowers in order not to develop an allergy that could make you start sneezing or you avoid inviting friends to your home because you are ashamed of your father's sneezes. This is an approach that is based on self-restraint and planning.

Giving in to a particular drive (the impulsive strategy)

Giving in to a particular drive encourages one to erase inhibitions. For example, you can actually encourage loud sneezing or, as Ori and his mother do in the story, you can laugh at the achoo.

The children should be taught to adopt this approach on condition that it does not jeopardize their health or their lives. Laughter is always good for one's health and giving in to the body's reactions will teach the children to know themselves better both physically and emotionally.

Contemplation (the mindfulness strategy), mindful listening

Teach the children to recognize the possibility of "both this and that," in other words, the possibility of both avoidance AND a total surrender to a particular drive. One can be on the alert, can make meticulous plans, can distance oneself and can practice avoidance, while, at the same time, one can also totally surrender to a particular drive. The children will thus learn that both sides exist in them and are even in conflict with one another and that it is possible to achieve an equilibrium between the two sides only if the children recognize the co-existence of both sides.

For example, in the story, Ori understands that his father's achoo is both "good" and "bad." Although it disturbs Ori, it is also the entertaining "melody" that characterizes his father.

You can discuss this issue with the children, explaining to them that the way to enable the two sides to peacefully coexist in them is through release and acceptance: release of the critical element and acceptance of the disturbing phenomenon as a part of life. For example, Ori's acceptance of his father's achoo "as is." This approach enables free choice and it is highly recommended.

Joining (the strategy of release, concession and the adoption of flexible positions)

As the expression says, "If you can't beat them, join them." The story illustrates how abandonment of the need to control and emerge the winner can lead to a solution. Instead of fighting the "big achoo" and his father, Ori learns in the story to "play" with the achoo, to enjoy and laugh at the funny sounds and faces that accompany the sneeze. Similarly, other children, your own children who are reading this book together with you, can discover that they are capable of adopting flexible positions and of abandoning rigid thinking, just as Ori at the end of the story accepts his father's achoo "as is."

The story takes your children on a journey that has various stations of coping with a conflict, each of which echoes one of the four strategies we have become familiar with. A discussion that emphasizes the adoption of flexible positions and the abandonment of rigid thinking against the background of the story can help them to relate to any conflict they will encounter in their lives as an intersection of options, from which they can choose the one that suits them best at that particular moment. In other words, they should see such conflicts as an opportunity to learn, to apply their judgment, to practice making decisions, to empower themselves and to grow, instead of viewing these conflicts as negative situations.

The serenity prayer contains the essence of all these approaches:

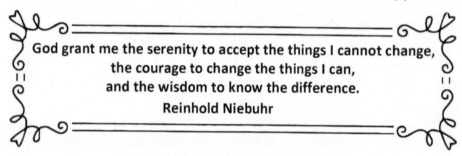

God grant me the serenity to accept the things I cannot change,
the courage to change the things I can,
and the wisdom to know the difference.
Reinhold Niebuhr

A similar idea appears in the book **A Selection of Pears from Shlomo Ibn Gabirol**, ch. 17 (Awareness), verse 2:

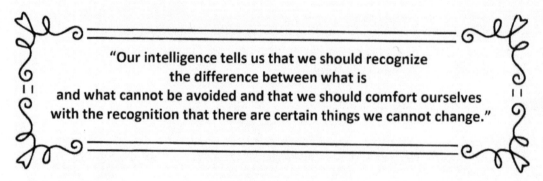

"Our intelligence tells us that we should recognize
the difference between what is
and what cannot be avoided and that we should comfort ourselves
with the recognition that there are certain things we cannot change."

Chapter 4 – Activities based on the story "The Big Achoo"

Recommended general activities to be conducted with your children.

Conversation – Who feels different in this story? How should we relate to the Other? What does Ori feel when he hears a loud noise? How does his father feel when he sees that his son does not understand him? In your opinion, who is suffering here from a sensory modulation difficulty? Ori? His father? Both of them? If you were in Ori's position, how would you solve this dilemma? And if you were in his father's position? Who should have made a change in his behavior? How should we relate to the disturbing behavior of one of our friends? How would you have liked this story to end? Did Ori's father accept his own father's difficulty? Did Ori accept his father's difficulty? Why? What could help Ori accept his father's achoo?

Language – What is meant by the "language of achoo"? This "language" is actually an image that represents loud noises. Invent your own language and start speaking it.

Drawing – Draw an achoo. A big achoo. A small achoo. A medium-sized achoo.

Turning the story into a play – Turn this story into a play. The director will narrate the story and the actors will play the roles of the characters in the story: Ori's father, Ori's mother and Ori. Represent the characters in different ways. For example, Ori and his father will exchange roles. Or, for example, Ori's father will sneeze in a different way. First, he will "hold in" his sneeze. Second, he will "swallow" it. Third, he will stop in the middle of a sneeze. Try to present the play or read out the story and then stop in the middle of the presentation or reading. How would you end the story? Present the story in pantomime.

Music – Write a song about sneezing and compose a suitable "sneezing melody." Play this melody on a piano, an organ, a xylophone and various percussion instruments. Record the melody you composed and then listen to the recording.

Movement and dance – Create a special movement to illustrate a sneeze and invent an Achoo dance.

A guide for parents, nursery school/kindergarten, teachers and therapists

How can I help my child?

When I see that my child is in a situation of psychomotor restlessness, I can help him/her in the following manner:

A bear hug – A hug that expresses acceptance and support signals to a child that his/her parent accepts his/her distress.

Applying pressure to your child's shoulders – A suitable method for young children.

Boxes of accessories - Encourage your child to engage in activity that provides him/her with stimuli. A suitable medium for this activity is the activities box you prepared at the beginning of this guide.

Mediation/Stage 1 – You must reflect your child: "I see that you are restless. You need a hug. You need some "hugging fuel" right?" Like toddlers who discover their independence in the preliminary stage preparing them to separate themselves from the parent as independent individuals, the child is distancing him/herself and wants his/her mother to "refuel" him/her.[5] A child with a sensory modulation difficulty may from time to time need a "fueling hug." In this first stage, it must be ascertained that the child knows that the adult required for a hug is available. The child will then discover that he/she can distance him/herself for an additional period of time until the next "fueling." A child with a sensory modulation difficulty needs a fueling hug, a strong stimulus, the application of deep pressure, the feeling that he/she is accepted. Later the child can be asked: "Do you need an energy hug? An extra-energy hug? A calming-down hug?"

Mediation/Stage 2 – We should reach an agreement with the child on a signal, such as the child's making the letter T (for Time Out) with his/her fingers, so that he/she can convey the message that he/she needs a break, that he/she is restless, and so that he can spend the break in the Zula Corner (the relaxation corner) or leave the room in order to calm down.

----

[5] Margaret Mahler, 1975.

Identification of a sensory need and provision for it – I will try to identify my child's sensory need; I will provide for that need in a suitable manner. For example, I will suggest that he/she take a toy/game out of the hand- or mouth-toy/game box.

Acceptance and containment (inclusion) – When I accept my child's difficulty, identify his/her needs and provide for those needs, his/her self-confidence will be reinforced, the symptoms of the difficulty will disappear or significantly diminish and his/her daily functioning will improve.

Gradual exposure and encouragement of my child to cope – Gradual exposure of the child to the stimulus he/she wants to avoid in order to encourage him/her to cope with the problem. It might be a good idea to repeat sentences like these: "Yes, you do have a modulation difficulty. Yes, you can cope with it (DO NOT USE THE WORD "BUT").

Staging and empowerment – We must provide a "stage" for children with modulation difficulties, while, at the same time, ignoring those difficulties and reinforcing their abilities. All children have certain gifts and skills that are relatively strong. We must identify their strong points and enable our children to express them. We will ask our children to prepare a short play, to sing, to play an instrument before an audience, and to create a "My Museum" corner in which they will put their artistic creations, and we will encourage them to engage in various sports; our goal must be to strengthen their self-confidence and to empower them.

A guide for children: "I have a difficulty to modulating myself"

Be aware of your difficulty and learn how to explain it to others.

You were born with well-developed senses, and you therefore have many advantages: You have very sharp senses that are always on the alert. You are sometimes very good when it comes to activities in open spaces. You sometimes stand out on nature excursions. You take in new environments quickly and you are among the first ones to react to them. And you might become a leader if you learn how to use the very sharp senses you were born with.

Your high sensitivity sometimes makes life difficult for you. This high sensitivity is called in professional language a sensory modulation difficulty (SMD). In the ordinary language of our daily lives, this means that you find it hard to make the shift from an activity you like (such as playing a video game or watching television) to an activity you don't like very much (such as doing your homework or listening to your teacher).

You can manage to modulate yourselves – Eight special magic methods

1. **Shifting gears (Making transitions):** Even when you are in the middle of an activity you enjoy, you can still make the shift to an activity that you enjoy less (entering the classroom, taking a shower, brushing your teeth). Making these shifts is challenging but it can be done.

2. **Taking a pause, stopping for a little while:** You know that it is hard for you to stop doing whatever you are doing at that moment. So that is why you should take a pause, stop doing whatever you are doing for a few seconds. This is different from stopping completely whatever you are doing. Just as you operate the music key on your computer, you can press your "Private Pause key" on your imaginary computer, you can stop for a few seconds and you can fulfill the task you have been asked to complete.

3. **Multisensory stimulation**: This means the activation of several of our sensory systems at the same time: for example, using our sense of smell and our sense of touch when we work with playdough, or using our sense of hearing and our sense of taste when we eat a carrot. When you use two or more of your senses at the same time, you are including multisensory activities in your daily routine, for instance, when you visit the playground, when you ride a tricycle or a bicycle, when you cook something, and so on.

4. **Zoom In, Zoom Out** – If there is a certain stimulus that bothers you (a sound, being touched or touching something, colors or smells), then imagine that you are continually zooming in and zooming out until the stimulus disappears. And always remember that the responsibility for modulating yourself rests with you and not with your environment!

5. **The principle of acceptance:** The more you oppose disturbing stimuli, the more they will bother you, and the less you oppose disturbing stimuli, the less they will bother you. The more you learn to accept these stimuli and to release them (that is, to stop opposing them), the less they will bother you. So you should teach yourself how to relax, to release (that is, to stop opposing something) and to accept.

6. **Turning something that bothers you into something that makes you laugh, or turning things inside out:** If a certain stimulus bothers you, try to laugh at it. For example, if someone sneezes next to you and his/her achoo bothers you, try sneezing with him/her at the same time and making a joke out of the whole thing.

7. **Breathing and relaxing:** Practice taking deep, long breaths in order to learn how to deal with disturbing stimuli and how to develop skills that will help you relax.

8. **The golden mean – choosing the middle course:** If you find it difficult to modulate yourself, it is highly recommended that you practice doing activities that are based on contrasts. For example, if you are told that you talk too loudly all the time, you should practice alternating between whispering and shouting until you modulate your voice. Afterwards, in order to maintain control of the tone of your voice, practice adjusting your voice gradually. Start whispering, then start talking at a medium level, then start talking in a loud voice, and then do the reverse. As far as sneezing is concerned, start sneezing loudly, then try a medium-sized sneeze and finally try a weak sneeze.

How to avoid "sensory incidents"

* We will develop our self-awareness: We will read about sensory modulation difficulties (SMD). We will learn about ourselves: Which one of my senses is very sensitive? Are two or more of my senses very sensitive? When do I feel very sensitive? What calms me down?

* We will prepare ourselves in advance: Or, to use the language of adults, we will learn how to adjust ourselves and to fine tune ourselves. In other words, we will learn how to identify in advance those situations in which "The alarm inside my body is operating at a very high level." So, for example, if a certain stimulus bothers us, we will try to avoid it as much as possible. For example, if a plane that is passing over us is making a lot of noise, we will stop up our ears. If a certain foul odor bothers us, we will open a window. If we want to go to a noisy party, we will arrive at the party with ear plugs in our ears. If the seams of a shirt we are wearing bother us, we will buy a shirt without seams.

* We will draw an invisible border around our body: Or, to use the language of adults, we will demarcate the boundary line between ourselves and our surroundings. We will draw an imaginary ring around our body and we will ask those in our surroundings to respect our personal space. (with little children, we can illustrate the concept of the imaginary ring with a hula hoop.)

* We will learn how to relax by means of a deep stimulus: Or, to use the language of adults, we will learn how to create a deep self-stimulus. For example, we will give ourselves a bear hug, we will hold on tight to our different joints, we will apply pressure to our shoulders, we will apply pressure to our different joints.

* Agreed signals for distancing ourselves: We will agree with our responsible adult (parent, teacher, instructor/counselor) on a hand signal – such as making a T with our two hands – that will be used to indicate that we have to take a break and to leave the room so that we can relax and then return to the room. After we receive permission to do so, we will distance ourselves from the place where we are now in order to neutralize the stimulus; after we have relaxed, we will return and again take part in the particular activity we were engaged in before.

* We will designate a Zula Corner where we can go and relax: When we feel that we have to go somewhere and relax, we will turn to a quiet corner and we will relax there. We will go to the Zula Corner; we will sit on a puff pillow or on a relaxing cushion or we will touch something that soothes us.

Conclusion

A conclusion is also a kind of modulation.

This book is about awareness of modulation, about sensory modulation difficulties in children, about how to provide for their modulation needs through mediation, about encouraging our children and about giving them the tools that can enable them to adjust to their surroundings. Since we cannot expect a child's environment to adjust itself to him/her, we must teach children with sensory modulation difficulties that they must adjust themselves to their environment. Children with these difficulties who are not treated for their problem might develop emotional and behavioral difficulties. Thus early detection of a sensory modulation difficulty and the provision of professional treatment are vital for the child's normative development.

We should always remember that an important element in dealing with a sensory modulation problem is acceptance of our child's disturbing behavior. When we accept his/her behavior, it will gradually disappear.

Appendix:
How to achieve a situation of equilibrium, how to attain the golden mean [6]

Maimonides discusses the balancing of human traits and argues that we must all arrive at an equilibrium of our traits, that we should distance ourselves from extreme behavior and that we should instead aspire to the golden mean. Human characteristics are located along a continuum between two poles that can be problematic: The positive pole is "surplus" and the negative pole is "shortage." We must try to achieve a balance with regard to all our traits as we seek the golden mean. The term "golden mean" refers to a middle ground that is equidistant from two extreme poles and refers to a balancing of our traits.

We will learn how to moderate our extreme traits if we can become familiar with the other side of each extreme trait. For example, we can learn how to balance a tendency toward squandering by means of parsimoniousness or penny-pinching, and vice versa. In order to balance our traits and to reach the golden mean, we must learn how to channel ourselves between the two extreme poles of any given trait.

At the same time, it is impossible to live solely according to the principle of the golden mean. In order to attain equilibrium, we must appropriate both extremes of the same trait and embody them in a single trait. Only by exercising the two extremes can we attain the golden mean, that is, only by doing so can we be prepared to become familiar with both extremes and then choose which one is the most appropriate for us. For example, while there are certain situations that demand that we adopt a rigid position, there are also certain situations that demand that we adopt a flexible position.

Maimonides' philosophy will not lead us to change our behavior if we do not go beyond a merely cognitive understanding of this idea. His philosophy demands that we exercise the two extremes of each trait in order to arrive at change and equilibrium. We must also teach this lesson to our children.

The contemplation approach (the mindfulness strategy) that was referred to earlier continues the philosophy of Maimonides, who did not believe in the "either-or" approach but instead believed in the "both sides" approach. The latter is a more comprehensive approach that relates to the two extremes of a single trait. We must look closely at every situation and must derive from our examination the "big picture" so that we can exercise our freedom of choice.

----
[6] Maimonides, Mishneh Torah, Laws Governing Opinions, Chapter 1, Laws 6-7.

Acknowledgments

In the Book of Psalms, we read "From all my teachers have I gained wisdom" (119:99); however, I have learned the most from my children and my clients. I want to express my deep gratitude to all the colleagues who extended to me their support, their assistance and their encouragement and who helped me turn this book from an idea into a reality. I want to thank them for their illuminations and wise comments.

I want to thank author Tzipora Dolan for her help as a literary consultant in the preparation of this book.

I want to express my gratitude to Miri Tal-Saban, Ph.D., occupational therapist, faculty member of the School of Occupational Therapy of the Hadassah University Medical Center and the Hebrew University of Jerusalem, and staff member of the Tze'adim Center in Ashdod; and Tomer Aharoni, M.Sc., biofeedback therapist, developer and writer for their her help as professional consultants in the preparation of the guidance chapter.

I want to thank Nicole Simon-Arkin, B.Sc., occupational therapist and staff member of the Keshet Parenting and Family Center, Yad Binyamin; Shlomit Elyassaf, M.A., Jerusalem-based music therapist ; Michal Zilbermintz, M.A., Tel Aviv-based music therapist , for their help as consultants in the preparation of this book.

I want to thank Dr. Cochavit Elefant, music therapist, lecturer and instructor, and Head of the School of Creative Arts Therapies, Faculty of Social Welfare and Health Sciences, University of Haifa, for teaching me how to play.

I want to express my thanks to Prof. Dorit Amir, music therapist, lecturer and instructor, and Head of the Music Therapy Program, Music Department, Bar-Ilan University, for teaching me how to provide therapy.

Finally, I want to thank the staff of the Manu Center in Rehovot: Patricia Sonino, art therapist, art instructor and artist, who taught me the art of contemplation; Drorit Azenkot, drama and art therapist; and animal-assisted therapists Naomi Bar-Ilan and Efrat Huberman, who taught me how to accept.

I love you all.

Dafna Warm

Epilogue: Experts' recommendations

In recent years there has been a growing awareness of the problem of impaired sensory modulation, a problem from which about ten percent of the population suffers, although there is still insufficient awareness of the problem's existence.

Sensory modulation refers to the process of reduction or intensification of the nervous activities in our body that is essential for the attainment of equilibrium in the central nervous system.

Sensory modulation difficulty is the impairment of our ability to modulate the intensity and nature of our reactions to sensory stimuli. This situation can at times lead to social and emotional problems.

In the book, **The Big Achoo**, by Dafna Warm (Sandler), a young boy, Ori, takes us on a journey that begins with the recognition of the existence of a problem, goes on to attempts to try various modulation techniques and reaches its climax when the most suitable method is found for Ori and his surroundings to cope with this problem.

The Big Achoo of is an important book that provides children, their parents and people in their educational setting with a large body of information and which is intended to increase awareness of this problem and its consequences. The promotion of awareness among all those who come in contact with the problem of sensory modulation impairment is vital for the encouragement of change and processes aimed at improving the functioning of children with that problem. The book delivers a message of confidence and hope to children regarding their abilities and helps them to understand themselves. The young reader who will identify with the chief protagonist of this story, Ori, will undergo a healing, beneficial emotional experience.

The feeling of release and acceptance achieved through *The Big Achoo* can contribute to the improvement of the quality of life for children with a sensory modulation problem, as well as for their parents and teachers. Furthermore, it can contribute to the attainment of emotional stability and normative social functioning, to an acceptance of personal responsibility and to a process of learning self-control.

Dafna Warm (Sandler), a music therapist who has treated generations of children, has written this important book from a child's perspective. In her book, she provides us with an important introduction to the problem of impaired sensory modulation and supplies us with highly effective and very creative solutions for dealing with this unique challenge.

The Big Achoo is a significant contribution to the empowerment of children and their therapists. It places the child and his/her needs at center stage, emphasizing the child's abilities and potential and accompanying its message with Mirel Goldenberg's captivating, charming and humorous illustrations.

Hannah Kaplan
Educational psychology specialist, instructor and group analyst

CPSIA information can be obtained
at www.ICGtesting.com
Printed in the USA
BVHW022312110521
607043BV00011B/1961